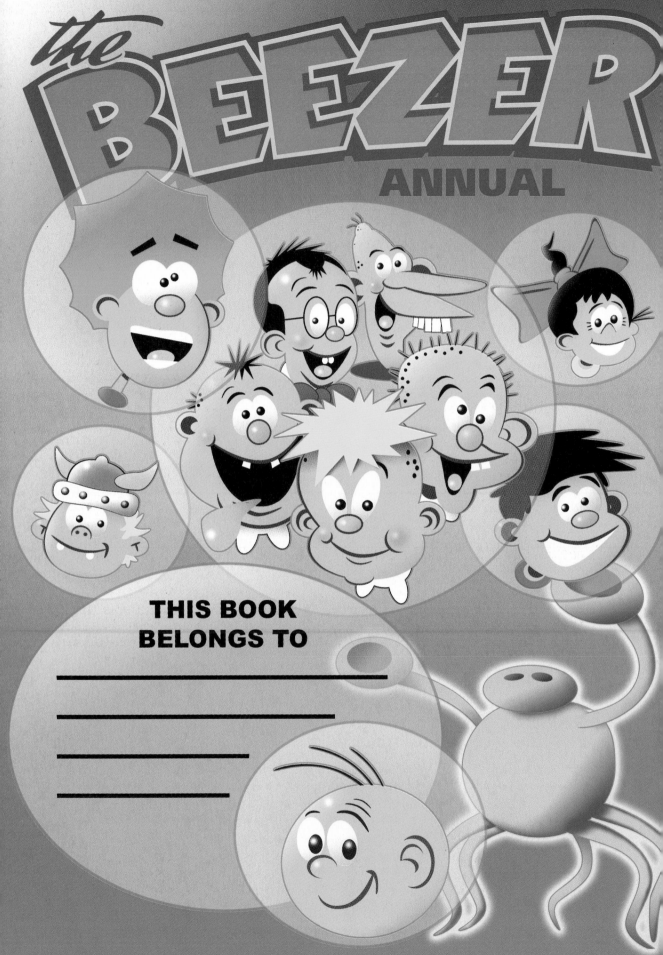

THIS BOOK
BELONGS TO

_____

_____

_____

Printed and Published in Great Britain by D. C. Thomson & Co., Ltd., 185 Fleet Street, London EC 4A 2HS.

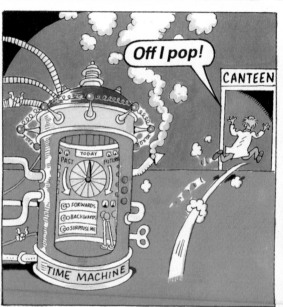

FROM THE DOMED CITY
A JELLYMAN SWIMS OUT-

HE ENCASES THE SUB.
IN A GIANT BUBBLE
FILLED WITH OXYGEN.

I CAN READ YOUR
THOUGHTS AND
LET YOU READ MINE.

WE APPRECIATE
THE HELP.

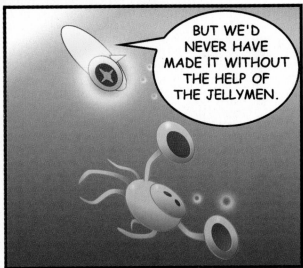

RUMBLE!

Oh, no! It's beginning!

Erk! Fred!

Gangway, Mum.

Minutes later —

This is harder than I thought!

Ow! My ears are hurting!

BOOT!

Take it back to the shop — I can't stand it anymore!

I'll get a refund at the Music Shop and then I'll buy something else!

One trip to town later —

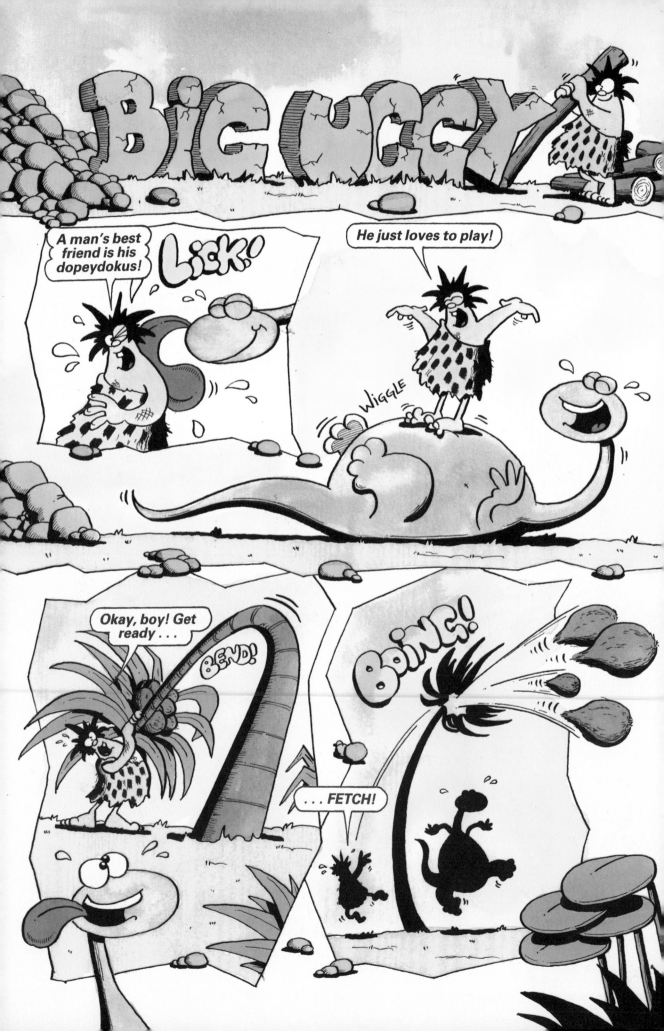

"Somebody's trying to get me with a fly swatter!"

"But they've no chance."

"I'm far too fly!"

"Too bad. Seat 'B' was already taken!"

"Never seen a bee like that before. I'll fly up and ask its name."

"Think its name is Chopper!"

"I'll visit the hive next door!"

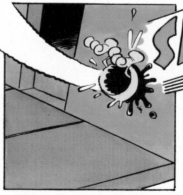

"They've moved the door!"

"Hope they have a dentist!"

FISHY GOINGS ON

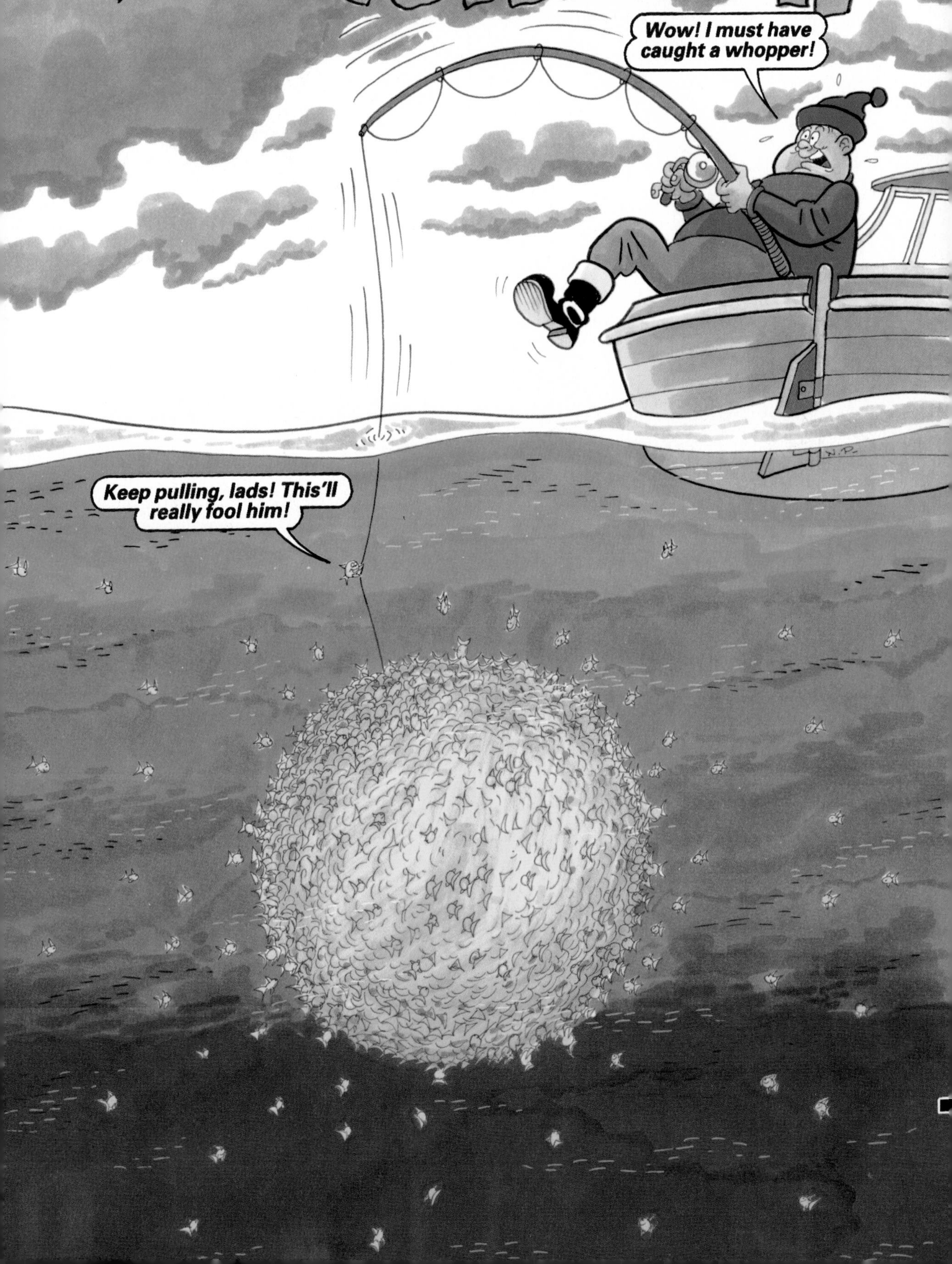

WILLY NILLY

Wandering Willy Nilly, as all attractive, intelligent and sophisticated people (otherwise known as Beezer Book readers) know, is a lad with a unique problem. His feet have minds of their own and lead him off in bizarre and puzzling directions. At this moment, a trip to buy liquorice sticks for his Auntie Doris finds Willy half way down a tin mine in Timbuktu. So, in order not to disappoint all frivolous feet fans with such a tedious tale, we're going to concentrate on the love of Willy's life – his girlfriend Dilly Dally.

Dilly was almost permanently penniless as her meagre pocket money was always being spent on new footwear. She was no fashion victim; it's just that her extensive wandering got through a lot of shoe leather. Realising that a paper round was impractical (her boyfriend, Willy, had been sacked from just such a job for delivering a copy of the Bognor Regis Bugle to a bewildered gibbon in Borneo), Dilly hit on dog walking as a way to expand her financial horizons.

After putting up several flyers in Minsk, Glasgow and Bombay, Dilly received her first commission from her next-door neighbour.

Taking a traumatised poodle home via the Ngorongoro crater in the Serengeti National Park was at best ill-advised, although those of us with well behaved feet should realise that Dilly was not being deliberately cruel – she just has no control of her tootsies.

After he was chased by a cheetah, trampled by a trumpeting tusker and mauled by a mongoose, the final humiliation for Lord Poochie-Poo the 63rd was being laughed at by a posse of spotted hyena puppies. Dilly quickly put him back on the leash and took him back to his anxious owner's home with only the slightest of detours through the Grand Canyon in Arizona.

ZOOM!

Sadly, her dog walking got off to a disastrous start when she walked Mrs Ponsonby's pampered pooch up Machupichu in Peru, from where he was carried off by a giant condor. In seeking a firmer hold, the condor dropped the yelping bundle of fluff into the Orinoco River, where he was given an interesting buzz cut by a group of hungry piranha fish. As the petrified poodle leapt from the water, fate took a hand and he landed straight into the arms of the distraught Dilly who was meandering home through the Amazon basin.

Mrs Ponsonby hardly recognised the dishevelled, quivering mutt that Dilly returned to her. He was no longer the well-groomed darling of the poodle world and, instead of the five pound fee Dilly expected to receive from a satisfied customer, she was presented with a bill for £20,000 for canine psychiatric counselling.

As the disconsolate Dilly headed for home, she met the returning Willy Nilly. Willy always seemed to know the right thing to say and quickly had Dilly smiling again when he told her, "never mind! Have a liquorice stick!"

THE END

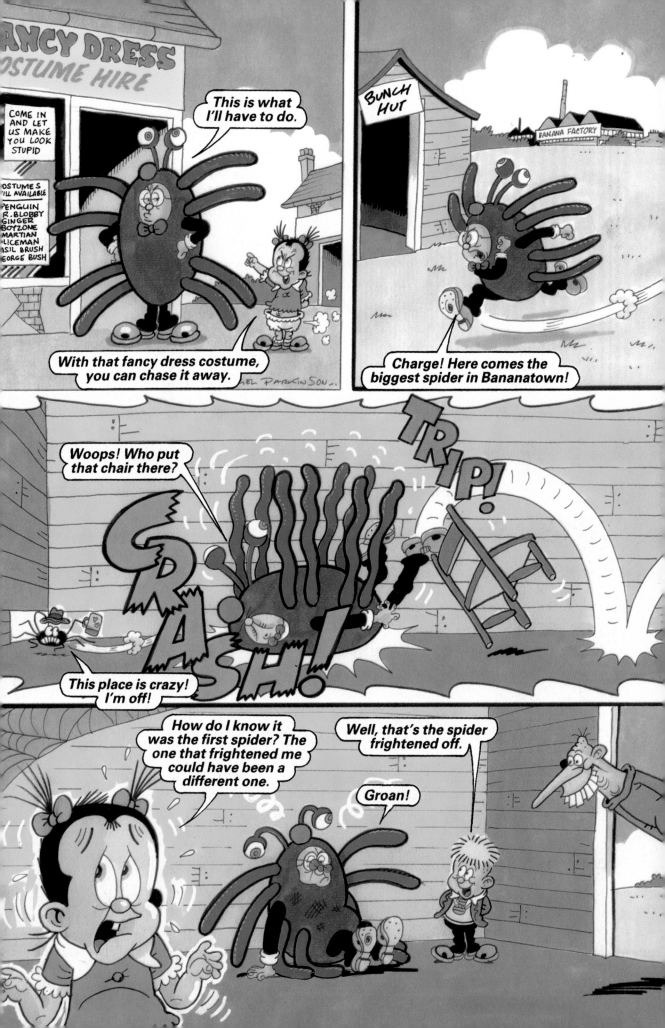